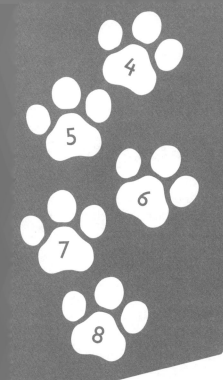

FIRST
COUNTING
Activity Book

Colour the paw print when you complete a page. See how far you've come!

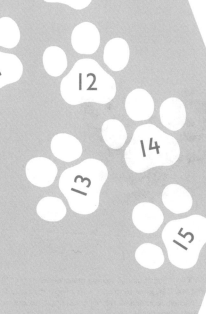

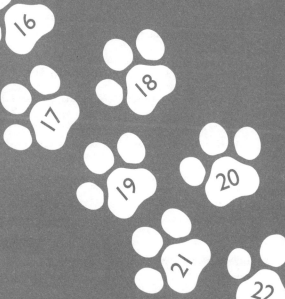

Author:
Carole Asquith

How to use this PAW Patrol Activity Book

This PAW Patrol First Counting Activity Book has been written to provide a gentle introduction to counting. You may need to introduce counters or other small objects to help your child understand the concepts of counting objects and adding and subtracting them. Try to use the following terms as you work through the book together: add, plus, take away, minus, more than, less than, equals, altogether, left over.

- Find a quiet, comfortable place to work.

- This book has been written in a logical order, so start at the first page and help your child to work their way through.

- Read out the instructions to your child where necessary and make sure that they know what to do.

- End each activity before your child gets tired in order to ensure that they will be keen to return to the activities next time.

- Help and encourage your child to check their own answers as they complete each activity. (Answers can be found on page 24.)

- Let your child return to their favourite pages after they have completed them. Talk about the activities they enjoyed and what they have learnt.

- Remember to give plenty of praise and encouragement.

- Once your child has completed all the activities in the book, reward them for their effort and achievement with the certificate on page 23.

Let the PAW Patrol help you with First Counting!

PAW Patrol – here to help!

ACKNOWLEDGEMENTS

Published by Collins
An imprint of HarperCollins*Publishers* Ltd
The News Building, 1 London Bridge Street, London SE1 9GF

HarperCollins*Publishers*
1st Floor, Watermarque Building, Ringsend Road, Dublin 4, Ireland

10 9 8 7 6 5 4

ISBN 978-0-00-846153-9

The author asserts the moral right to be identified as the author of this work. All rights reserved. No part of this publication may be reproduced, stored in a retrieval system, or transmitted, in any form or by any means, electronic, mechanical, photocopying, recording or otherwise, without the prior permission of Collins.

British Library Cataloguing in Publication Data

A Catalogue record for this publication is available from the British library.

© Spin Master Ltd. ™PAW Patrol and all related titles, logos, characters; and SPIN MASTER logo are trademarks of Spin Master Ltd. Used under license. Nickelodeon and all related titles and logos are trademarks of Viacom International Inc.

Author: Carole Asquith
Publisher: Fiona McGlade
Project editor: Katie Galloway
Cover design: Sarah Duxbury
Internal design: Ian Wrigley
Layout: Rose & Thorn Creative Services Ltd
Production: Karen Nulty
Printed in Great Britain by Martins the Printers

Contents

Numbers 0–10

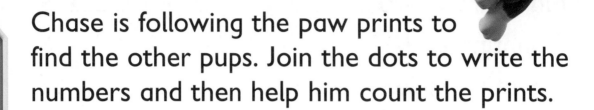

Chase is following the paw prints to find the other pups. Join the dots to write the numbers and then help him count the prints.

0

1

 2

3

 4

5

 6

7

 8

9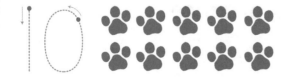

10

Numbers 11–20

Rubble is counting badges for the pups. Join the dots to write the numbers and then help him count the badges.

11

12

13

14

15

16

17

18

19

20

Counting to 10

Farmer Yumi is counting the vegetables in her vegetable patch. Help her count them by drawing lines to match the pictures to the numbers.

1

2

3

4

5

6

7

8

9

10

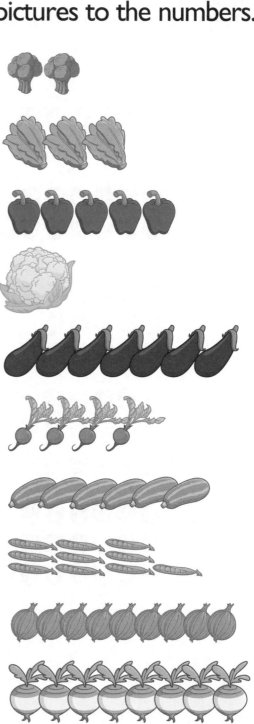

Counting to 20

Ryder is getting treats for himself and the pups. Help him count them by drawing lines to match the pictures to the numbers.

11

12

13

14

15

16

17

18

19

20

How many?

Count the apples on each tree and write the number in the box.

Count the apples in each row. Circle the correct number.

1   2   3   4   5   6   7   8   9   10

1   2   3   4   5   6   7   8   9   10

How many altogether?

How many presents can you count altogether?

How many paw prints can you count altogether?

How many books can you count altogether?

More and less

Ryder is putting treats into the pups' bowls.
Tick the bowl that has more treats.

Chase   Rubble   Zuma

Which pup has less (fewer) balloons?
Tick the pup who has less (fewer) balloons.

Adding 1

Draw one more cookie. How many are there altogether? Write the number in the box.

Count the flasks. Say the sum out loud.

 and

makes

Adding 2

Finish the sum by drawing the total number of paw prints.

 and

makes

Count each set of bowls. Add them together and write the total.

  and

makes

Adding 3

Count each set of teddy bears. Add them together and write the total.

 and

makes

Count each set of toy cats. Add them together and write the total.

   and

makes

Adding 4

Count the snowboards and write the total number in the box.

 and

1 + 4 =

Count the penguins and write the total number in the box.

 and

4 + 1 =

Adding 5

Colour 5 more rabbits.

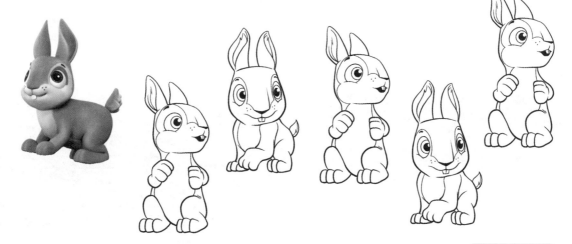

How many rabbits are there altogether?

Count the trees. Write the numbers in the boxes.

   and      makes

   +   =

Taking away 1

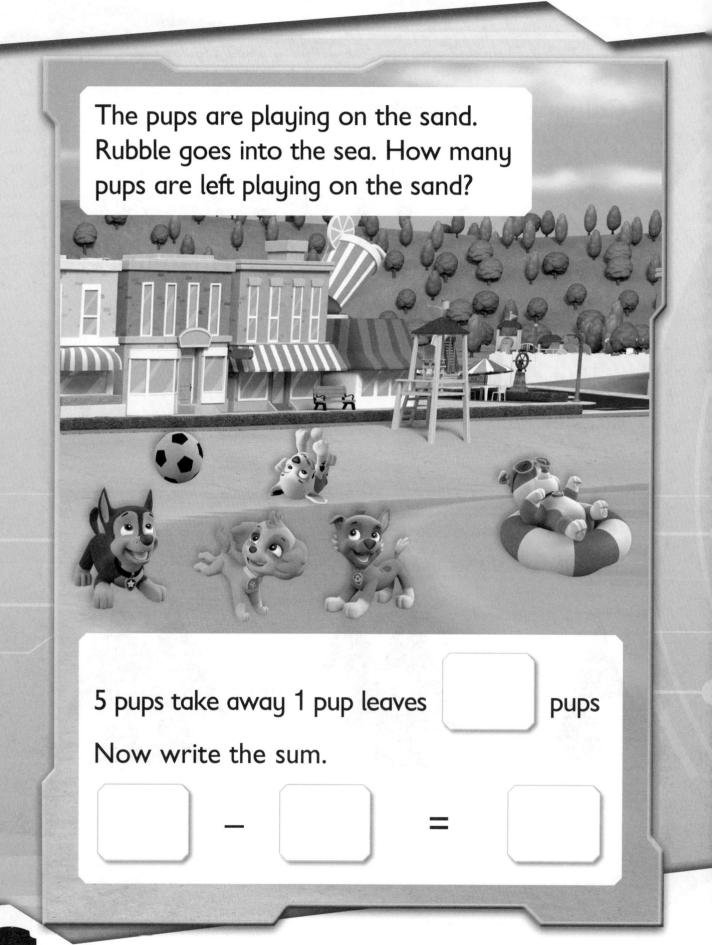

The pups are playing on the sand. Rubble goes into the sea. How many pups are left playing on the sand?

5 pups take away 1 pup leaves ⬜ pups

Now write the sum.

⬜ — ⬜ = ⬜

Taking away 2

Count the flowers. Cross 2 out.
How many are left?

Count the apples on
the first tree.

When the wind blew,
2 apples fell off.

Count the apples on the second tree to see
how many are left.

Now write the sum.

☐ – ☐ = ☐

Taking away 3

Help the pups to work out how many balls are left when 3 are taken away.

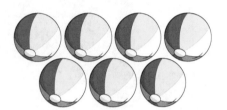   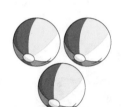

7 — 3 = [ ]

9 — 3 = [ ]

6 — 3 = [ ]

4 — 3 = [ ]

Taking away 4

Count the rabbits in the Lookout garden. Cross 4 out. How many are left?

Count the umbrellas on the beach. Cross 4 out. How many are left? Complete the sum.

8 – 4 =

Taking away 5

Captain Turbot is sailing his boat in Adventure Bay and counting the things he sees.

Complete the sums by crossing out the number of objects to take away and writing how many are left.

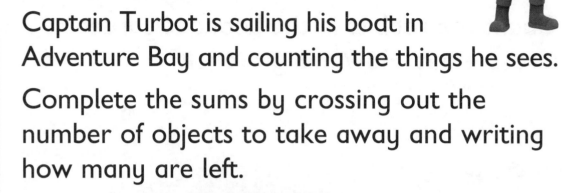

$$8 - 5 = \boxed{}$$

$$10 - 5 = \boxed{}$$

Counting practice

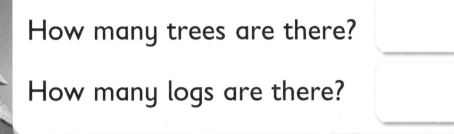

How many trees are there?

How many logs are there?

How many penguins are on sledges?

How many penguins are **not** on sledges?

Adding and taking away practice

Count the pups and write the number in the first box. Then add 2. How many pups are there altogether?

[ ] **+ 2 =** [ ]

Farmer Yumi has grown 8 apples but she eats 4. How many are left?

 **8 – 4 =** [ ]

6 whales are spotted near Seal Island. 3 go under the water. How many are left?

 **6 – 3 =** [ ]

This badge is awarded to

....

Age ....

For successfully completing

PAW Patrol First Counting Activity Book

Date ....

Signed ....

Well done!

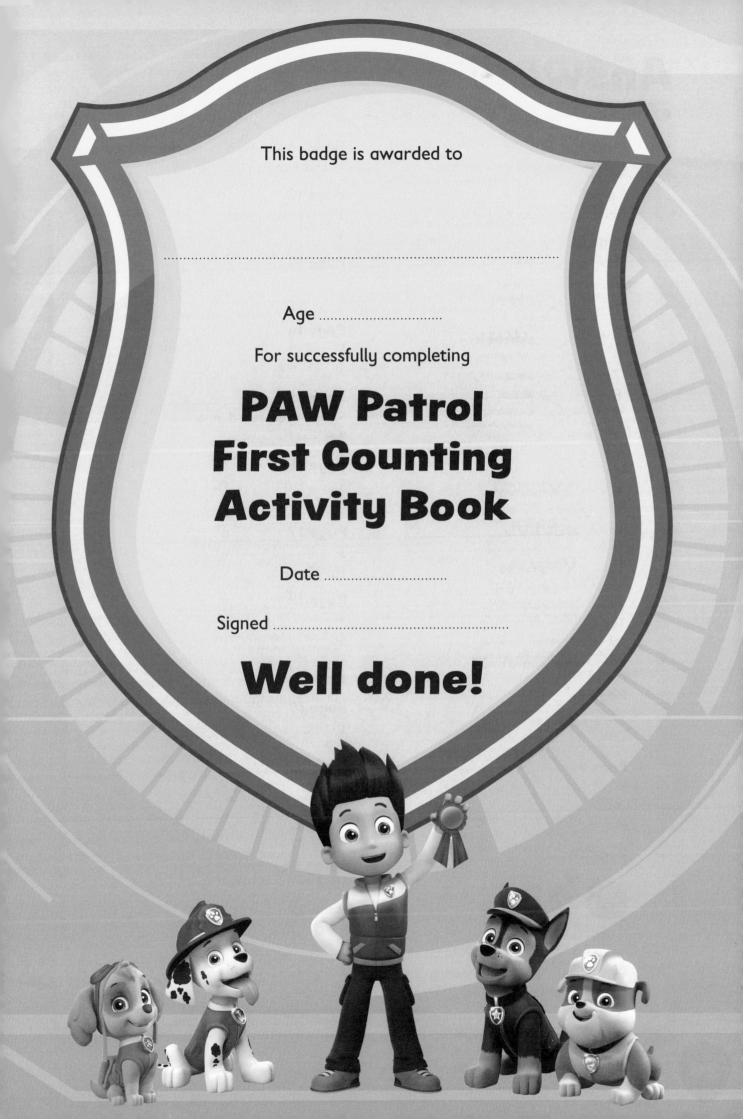

Answers

Page 4
Child to join dots on numbers.

Page 5
Child to join dots on numbers.

Page 6

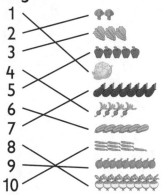

Page 7

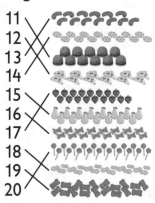

Page 8
10, 6, 11, 4, 12, 8
7, 4

Page 9
5
14
8

Page 10

Page 11
1 cookie drawn; 2

Flasks counted and sum said out loud
(1 and 1 makes 2).

Page 12
3 paw prints drawn.
4

Page 13
4
4

Page 14
5
5

Page 15
5 rabbits coloured in; 6
2 + 5 = 7

Page 16
4
5 − 1 = 4

Page 17
3
10 − 2 = 8

Page 18
4
6
3
1

Page 19
1
4

Page 20
3
5

Page 21
6, 3
10, 2

Page 22
8 + 2 = 10
4
3